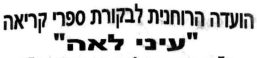

הועדה הרוחנית לבקורת ספרי קריאה

"עיני לאה"

ע"ש הרבנית לאה אויערבך ע"ה

בנשיאות הגאון ר' ישראל גנס שליט"א

ירושלים עיה"ק 050-4122756

I hereby affirm that a representative of the committee reviewed the Hebrew edition of the book *Just Imagine! We're Going to the Beis Hamikdash*, written by M. Safra, and has found it suitable and recommended for the entire family — both young and old.

Chazal point out for us in Maseches Sukkah (*perek* 5, *mishnah* 1): "Anyone who never saw the *simchas beis hasho'evah*, has never seen *simchah* in his life." That is to say, all the various *simchos* that a person enjoys in his life cannot compare to the *simchah* at the Beis Hamikdash. If that is the case, then we who have not merited experiencing the *simchah* there, cannot understand it. In this book the author attempts to bring us into the uniquely exalted and uplifting atmosphere that existed in Yerushalayim during the Yom Tov of Sukkos in the times of the Beis Hamikdash.

As our Sages have written, when *Hakadosh Baruch Hu* will come in His great mercy, to comfort Am Yisrael, there will no consolation or *simchah* other than the Beis Hamikdash. All that remains is for us to daven to merit the *simchah* of the Beis Hamikdash speedily in our days. Amen.

Since the written word serves as an influential educational tool, this committee is of vital importance, and is sorely needed in a generation where anyone wielding a pen can easily—due to technological developments—publish anything they please.

HaRav Yisrael Gans, *shlita*

Just Imagine! We're Going to the Beis Hamikdash
Copyright © 2016 by Tfutza Publications
ISBN: 978-1-60091-464-5

Tfutza
Publications

P.O.B. 50036
Beitar Illit 90500
Tel: 972-2-650-9400
Tfutza1@gmail.com

First printed in Hebrew as *Ilu V'kilu: V'samachta b'chagecha...v'hayisa ach sameach*

Written by M. Safra
Cover Design and Illustrations by Yaakov Hanon
Translated by Ruti Cywiak
Torah Editor: Rav A. Holzer
Edited by Sara Miriam Gross
Proofread by Miriam Deutscher
Typeset by Mrs. B. Soloveichik

Distributed by:
Israel Bookshop Publications
501 Prospect Street
Lakewood, NJ 08701
Tel: (732) 901-3009
Fax: (732) 901-4012
www.israelbookshoppublications.com
info@israelbookshoppublications.com

Printed in Israel

Distributed in Israel by:	Distributed in Europe by:	Distributed in Australia by:	Distributed in S. Africa by:
Tfutza Publications	Lehmanns	Gold's Book & Gift Company	Kollel Bookshop
(02) 650-9400	Unit E Viking Industrial Park	3-13 William Street	Ivy Common
	Rolling Mill Road,	Balaclava 3183	107 William Rd, Norwood
	Jarrow, Tyne & Wear NE32 3DP	613-9527-8775	Johannesburg 2192
	44-191-430-0333		27-11-728-1822

Just Imagine!

WE'RE GOING TO THE BEIS HAMIKDASH

JERUSALEM'S RESIDENTS WELCOME THE OLEI REGEL!

An original, fascinating portrayal of the simchah in Yerushalayim, during the Yom Tov of Sukkos

Tfutza Publications

WRITTEN BY M. SAFRA ◆ ILLUSTRATED BY YAAKOV HANON

Introduction

Dear Children,

Many years ago, when the Beis Hamikdash was standing, there was a celebration in Yerushalayim. It was called the *simchas beis hasho'evah*. The joy then was so great that Chazal teach us that anyone who did not see the *simchas beis hasho'evah* – never saw true joy in his life!

Perhaps you want to reply that today there are also *simchas beis hasho'evah* celebrations in almost every shul, and you've participated in many such events... But truth be told, the *simchah* that we have today is not the same – it's only a commemoration of the real *simchas beis hasho'evah*, which took place in the Beis Hamikdash and from which people drew purity and *ruach hakodesh*, and were uplifted for the entire year!

Halevai, we should merit to see that wondrous *simchas beis hasho'evah* even once! *Halevai* we should merit it speedily in our days, in the third Beis Hamikdash that will come down from the Heavens in fire! But in the meantime, let us try to imagine how the *simchah* would look, and how preparations for the entire Yom Tov of Sukkos would take place in Yerushalayim, if the Beis Hamikdash were standing today...

Without a doubt, the *simchas beis hasho'evah* today would look exactly the way it did back then, in the Beis Hamikdash. In the Palace of the King, there is no room for changes of any kind...The Leviim would play on the same melodious instruments that they played thousands of years ago, and the righteous Yidden would dance the same dances of purity and holiness in honor of the King of Kings...

But can we possibly imagine how Yerushalayim looked when many millions of people came into the city with their *korbanos* in order to celebrate with Hashem in His city and His Mikdash? Can we imagine what an elevated atmosphere of purity would spread throughout the whole city as the Yom Tov drew nearer? It's no doubt quite difficult to describe...

The book you are holding can help a little bit to illustrate this wonderful scene, to try to help us feel a bit of the atmosphere of the genuine, tangible *simchah* that was apparent in every corner of the holy city. As you read, you will probably come across unfamiliar terms. We created a Glossary on page 56 to help you better understand this important subject. Perhaps, if we truly understand the magnitude of the loss, we will know how to daven properly before our Father in Heaven to return the Beis Hamikdash and the Holy City to us, speedily in our days. And who knows? Perhaps this year, we will merit celebrating Sukkos in the newly rebuilt Beis Hamikdash!!

M. Safra

Motzaei Yom Kippur

Tatty! I'm so happy that the leshon zehoris turned white!

So am I, Shimmy...It's a tremendous simchah! It means that Hashem has forgiven us for all our sins this Yom Kippur, and that the avodah of the Kohen Gadol was accepted!

Well, with a tzaddik like Rav Yirmiyahu HaKohen for a Kohen Gadol, it's really not a surprise...

Yes, the Kohen Gadol in our time really is a tzaddik... Do you know that it wasn't always like that, Shimmy? There were years when the Kohen Gadol would pay money to get appointed!

What??

SPLASH

Yes indeed...Unfortunately, there were times like that...

And what happened?

Terrible things happened! Each year, the Kohen Gadol, who wasn't a real tzaddik, would not emerge alive from the Kodesh Hakodashim! Only a Kohen Gadol who is a tzaddik can enter the Kodesh Hakodashim and come out safely.

So each year there was a new Kohen Gadol???

That's right Shimmy...

That's so sad!

It sure is...But why think about sad things now? The main thing is we were zocheh and the Kohen Gadol came out alive from the Kodesh Hakodashim, which shows us that he's a real tzaddik!

Is that why everyone was so happy when they saw him come out of the Kodesh Hakodashim?

Exactly!

And that's why everyone accompanied him home, singing all the way, after the avodah?

Exactly!

And now I want to ask you something, Shimmy...

Yes, Tatty?

Do you have energy?

Sure I have energy! After all, I didn't fast today...

So what do you think about helping me start building our sukkah???

I think that's a great idea!

A short time later...

Tatty, do you think all the guests will fit into our little sukkah???

I can't wait for Yom Tov to start...

Shimmy, it's time to go to sleep now. Tomorrow I'll take you to the Beis Hamikdash where you'll be able to see the preparations that have begun for the simchas beis hasho'evah!

Wow! But what about our sukkah? When will we finish building it?

Don't worry... We have four more days until Sukkos... B'ezras Hashem we'll get it all done.

The next morning...

Tatty, you said we'd go to the Beis Hamikdash today to see the preparations for the simchas beis hasho'evah!

Oh, I see you've gotten up early.

I sure did! I'm so excited!

Alright. I'm going out to daven now, and you can come along...When we finish davening we'll go through the arba minim market and then we'll head for the Beis Hamikdash...

Wow!!! I'll be right there!!!

Unbelievable... Shimmy is moving so fast this morning!!!

A few hours later...

ARBA MINIM MARKET

A short time later...

They are bringing the women's section.

The women's section? Wait a minute—but there already is a women's section in the Beis Hamikdash.

Although there's a part of the Beis Hamikdash called the Ezras Nashim, both men and women are allowed inside it during the year at different times..

Since the Ezras Nashim is used for the simchas beis hasho'evah, they need a different women's section during Sukkos.

But where is there room for such a thing? Do they divide the Azarah in half?

Of course not...The women's section is being built at the height of the Azarah, near the walls, from where the women can see the simchas beis hasho'evah

Wait a minute...I don't understand...The ladies' section is built from scratch each year?

Exactly!!!

But why?

Very simple: Nothing about the shape of the Beis Hamikdash can be changed. On the other hand, *tzniyus* must be maintained during the *simchas beis hasho'evah*...Therefore, each year, a special ladies' section is built only for Sukkos, and right after Yom Tov, it is taken apart.

Why are so many trucks needed to build this women's section?

Because it is built on the walls of the *Ezras Nashim* which is 135 *amos* by 135 *amos*, meaning, about 230 feet by 230 feet! If you do the math, you'll realize that's a very big area...

And how do the women get into this section?

Through special gates, one at the north and one at the south. After those gates, there are steps that lead straight to the ladies' section.

Come, let's get a bit closer to the trucks and maybe you'll be able to understand exactly how it looks...

Great!

Look, Shimmy. Now do you understand better?

These balconies are placed on stone stakes that stick out of the walls of the *Ezras Nashim*, and the women can stand on these stairs and see the *simchas beis hasho'evah* without anyone else seeing them.

Can we watch how they put these balconies into place?

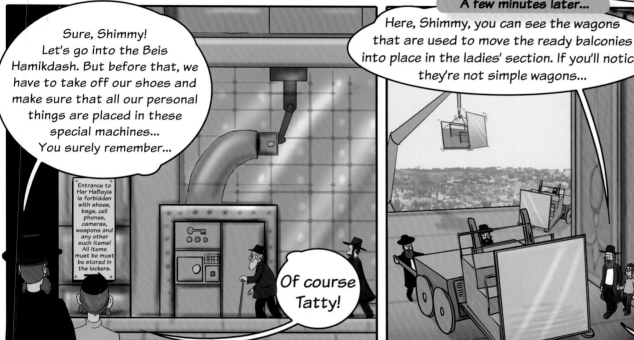

Sure, Shimmy! Let's go into the Beis Hamikdash. But before that, we have to take off our shoes and make sure that all our personal things are placed in these special machines... You surely remember...

Entrance to Har HaBayis is forbidden with shoes, bags, cell phones, cameras, weapons and any other such items! All items must be must be stored in the lockers.

Of course Tatty!

A few minutes later...

Here, Shimmy, you can see the wagons that are used to move the ready balconies into place in the ladies' section. If you'll notice, they're not simple wagons...

AMAZING!!!

These are wagons with special forklifts that are made specifically for this purpose. They can lift the balconies up and place them in the right spot!

A short time later...

Let's follow the wagons onto Har Habayis...And from this moment on we have to remember the special holiness of this site, and to behave accordingly!

I remember, Tatty. It's not the first time I'm going into the Beis Hamikdash.

Still, it's very important, and an extra reminder never hurts.

We're going in through the Eastern gate to the *Ezras Nashim*, Shimmy. Pay attention! This is a very holy place and we have to be extremely respectful!

Of course, Tatty! Look, even the workers who are pushing the wagons are working in silence!

Indeed. Only people who understand the *kedushah* of the site are hired for this kind of work.

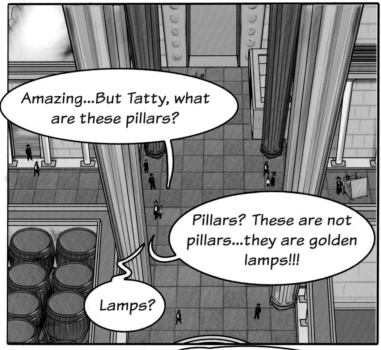

ALL of Yerushalayim??

Wait a minute...Where are those people going with ladders?

Yes, Shimmy, all of Yerushalayim!

Oh, I see we got here at just the right time! If I'm not mistaken, those are young Kohanim who are bringing ladders to be able to practice climbing to the top, to fill the lamps with oil from their jugs.

What??? They're going to climb to the top of the lamps on these ladders???

Exactly! How else do you think they get filled with oil?

Honestly, I didn't really think about it, but it sure looks scary!!!

It sure does...and that's why they practice! There's no doubt that it's a hard job, that requires lots of courage and also strength...But don't worry...I've never heard of any accidents happening when the young Kohanim climb the ladders.

I don't believe it! They're going to climb up those ladders holding those huge jugs???

Exactly. And we'll wait here now so you can see it all for yourself.

Wow!!

They're so brave!! How are they not afraid??

I think that they are so excited to have the zechus of preparing the lamps for the simchah in the Beis Hamikdash that they don't feel anything else!!!

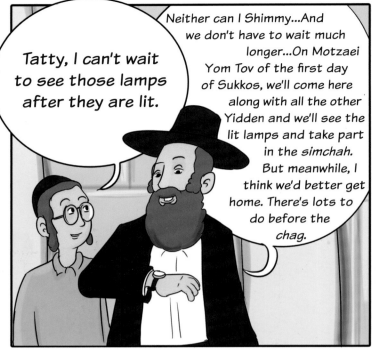

Tatty, I can't wait to see those lamps after they are lit.

Neither can I Shimmy...And we don't have to wait much longer...On Motzaei Yom Tov of the first day of Sukkos, we'll come here along with all the other Yidden and we'll see the lit lamps and take part in the simchah. But meanwhile, I think we'd better get home. There's lots to do before the chag.

A short time later...

Shimmy, I think we'll get off at the next stop...

But why, Tatty? We're still far from home...

That's right but I want to pass through the livestock market...

We have to buy animals for the Olas Hare'iyah, Shalmei Chagigah and Shalmei Simchah.

Yay!!! I love going to the livestock market. It's amazing that it's so clean and organized even though animals are being sold there....

That's right! It's in Yerushalayim, the holy city of the Mikdash... It can't be dirty and soiled...

It's really busy here today, Tatty, isn't it?

Certainly is. After all, the chag is coming, and everyone needs olos and shelamim! Besides, the many guests coming to Yerushalayim use the opportunity to bring korbanos nedarim and nedavos that they pledged since Shavuous...

I hope that there are sheep left for us...

Of course there are. The dealers here know that demand goes up and they prepare accordingly. Look at all those trucks full of sheep and cows waiting to be unloaded!

Our korbanos are the most tamim!

COW-CENTER

MOST MEHUDAR

Lambs by Lamchik

Under the hashgachah of Rabbi Yakelovitz, shlita

MEHADRIN MIN HAMEHADRIN

Korbanos with a guarantee!! The only ones on the market!!!

The finest korban!!! Come and buy a mehudar korban!!!

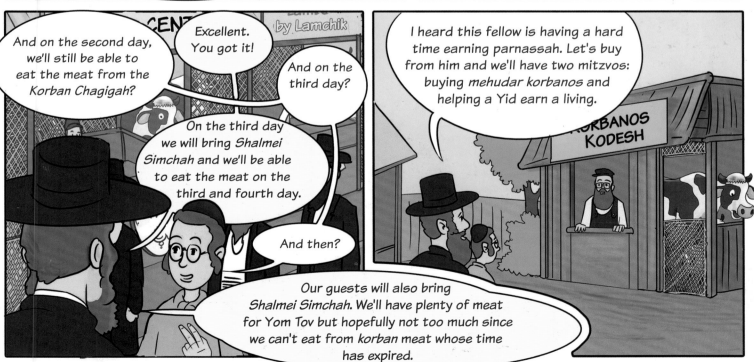

A short time later...

A short time later...

Number 328 to Room 6

It's our turn! Let's go in...

I see that you found excellent, hefty animals!

We had a lot of *siyata diShmaya*...I just hope they are kosher and whole...

What are they for?

The cow is for the *Olas Re'iyah* and the sheep are for *Korban Chagigah* and *Shalmei Simchah*.

Excellent... excellent...

A few minutes later...

All the animals are kosher and *mehudar*! Have a *chag sameach*, dear Yidden!

Thank you honored Rav.

Now all we have to do is pay and take the animals home... I think I'm going to ask for home delivery this time... After all, we have three animals!

I don't mind taking them with us!

Still, it will be a bit complicated, Shimmy... Don't worry. I trust the dealer; he is a *yarei Shamayim* and will watch over the animals until they get to our house.

A moment later

My friend, everything is fine! The Rav approved the animals and said they are *mehudar*! How much do I owe you?

I don't know... Let's weigh the animals and find out.

The bill comes to 5,000 shekels for the cow, and 1,000 for each of the sheep, or seven thousand in all.

No problem...These are expenses for Shabbos and Yom Tov, and Hashem repays us – especially when it's for korbanos!

Naturally. Do you want home delivery?

I think so...

No problem at all...

Write your address down here, and the animals will be delivered in the next few hours.

Three days later...

Good morning, Shimmy! I think you'll want to get up...

What time is it, Tatty?

It's six in the morning, but it's Erev Yom Tov, as I'm sure you remember, and we've got so much to do...

I'm getting up right away, Tatty.

A moment later...

Good for you... I see you really hurried! You can come with me to daven and then we will start preparing for Yom Tov.

What's left to do?

We need to make room in the sukkah for all the guests! Uncle Shlomo is coming today with his children, and so is Uncle Avrum with his whole family.

Besides them, we'll have a few guests who are not family...

How is everyone going to fit?

Don't worry, you'll see...

I love these days before Sukkos!! There are so many interesting things to see on the street.

There sure are...You can tell Yom Tov is coming, and it is so heartwarming to see!!

After davening...

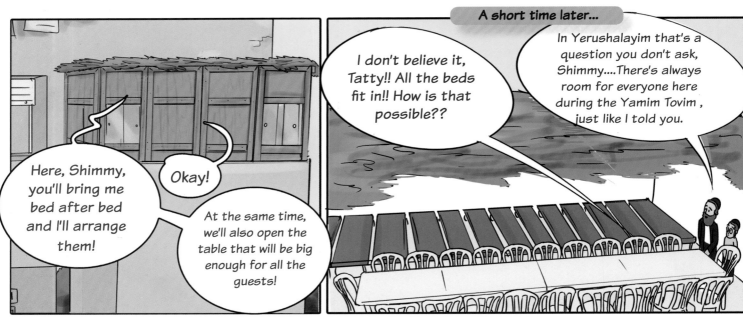

A few hours later...

VESAMACHTA BECHAGECHA VEHAYISA ACH SAMEACH!!!

Uncle Avrum, it's so nice to be happy and sing together, but I think we'd better get to sleep...We have to get up very early if we want to get to the Beis Hamikdash on time, don't we?

You're absolutely right.

SHIR HAMAALOS...

One minute, Tatty, what time do we have to get to the Beis Hamikdash tomorrow?

The question is not when we have to, but when we *want to*! And we want to get there before dawn to join the procession that goes out to the Shiloach Spring to draw the water!

Wow!!! Yay!!!

And now, everyone has to go to sleep!!! The timer is shutting off the lights in just a few minutes...

A few hours later...

Boys, it's time to get up.

What? Is it morning already???

Not at all... It's two o'clock, but when it is morning, we'll want to be at the Beis Hamikdash already!

We're getting up right away!

A short time later...

Now we all walk out very quietly, so we don't wake up everyone else! The little children can't come with us... It's too far. Don't forget the *arba minim*!

Now children, we'll take off our shoes and give all our personal items to the guards at the entrance...Of course the machines don't work on Yom Tov, so they do manual security checks.

Every family gets one locker! Please be considerate of others!!!

Here's your locker number: 3765! Don't lose the ticket because without it you won't be able to claim your things!!

Of course, that makes sense.

Right...We'll be very careful with it.

Now we will enter Har Habayis and tie up the animals in the right place. Then we can join the procession going out to the Shiloach Spring! I think we've gotten here in time to see everything!!

I think we'd better hurry, right?

It's always good to hurry to do mitzvos...

A few minutes later...

Kohanim stand up for your avodah, Leviim to the duchanim and Yisrael to your places!!!

That's the announcement signaling the start of today's avodah. It's probably daybreak, when the roosters crow, and the procession is about to leave. Let's hurry!

But first we should probably put our arba minim in the shul in the Har Habayis.

Sure...

TOOO---TOOO-TO-TO-TO-TO TOOO---TOOO-TO-TO-TO-TO-TO TOOO---TOOO-TO-TO-TO-TO-TO!!!!

There's the procession! Do you see the Kohanim with the trumpets standing at the Nikanor Gates?

I sure do!

About an hour later...

We're getting close to the Shiloach Spring!

Why can't we just draw water from this stream that flows from the spring?

Because the water needs to be drawn from the source of the spring, not from a runoff stream.

Tatty, where is Uncle Avrum and his family? And where is Uncle Shlomo?

We'll meet after we finish bringing all the korbanos so we can go home together...It would be too complicated to try and walk together as one group the whole day.

Here we are, at the spring. This is where the Shiloach Spring flows from the ground, and you can see how the Kohen is filling a golden bowl that contains three lugim, which is about one quart...

L'kavod mitzvas nisuch hamayim !

Now we're going to return to the Beis Hamikdash!!!

Tatty, where is the mitzvah of nisuch hamayim written in the Torah?

It's not. It was given to Moshe at Har Sinai, orally. It's called "halachah l'Moshe miSinai." That's why the Tzedokim, who lived in the days of the Mishnah, did not believe in this mitzvah — because they didn't believe in Torah Sheba'al Peh. They were kofrim, heretics!

What reshaim!

Exactly...Unfortunately, one year there was a Tzedoki Kohen and no one knew about it. He poured the water over his feet instead of into the special vessel for this purpose in the Beis Hamikdash...

Oh, my!!!

The people were so angry they threw their esrogim at him. From then on the Kohen who pours the water raises his right hand, so that everyone can see exactly where he is pouring it!

Look, we're already at the Beis Hamikdash...Dawn is breaking, and the Kohanim are beginning their avodah for the day!!!

One minute, Tatty...Where are we going? Why aren't we heading for the east gate, like before?

Oh, that's because the water for nisuch hamayim is brought in through a special gate that is opened only for this purpose and only on Sukkos. It's called the Shaar Hamayim, the Water Gate. This gate is south of the Ezras Kohanim, across from the western part of the ramp of the mizbeach, and that's where we're going now.

Tatty, if we stand opposite the gate, will we be able to see the Mizbeach?

Sure! And you'll be able to see a few other very interesting things too.

So let's walk quickly so we can catch a good spot!

Hold my hand and we'll hurry towards the gate...

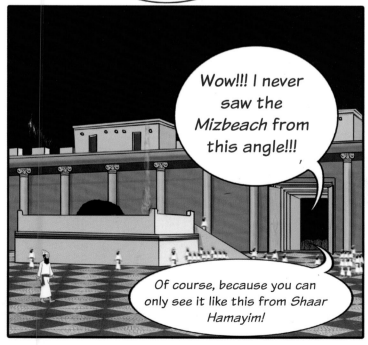

Wow!!! I never saw the Mizbeach from this angle!!!

Of course, because you can only see it like this from Shaar Hamayim!

Look, the Kohen who received the terumas hadeshen is getting off the Mizbeach holding a silver machtah, a special pan, with the deshen that he took from the fire! Soon there will be another miracle!

Miracle? Which one??

Wait and you'll see for yourself!

The Kohanim are coming with the parts of the *Tamid*, with the *Minchas Hatamid*, and the *Minchas Hachavisin* of the Kohen Gadol, and with the wine of the *nesachim* that they pour on the *Korban Tamid*.

Now the Kohanim will salt the parts of the sheep and then daven a special *nusach* in the *Lishkas Hagazis*. Let's hurry to *toivel* in the *mikveh* and go back to the *Azarah*. We don't want to miss *Birkas Kohanim*!

A short time later...

Here we are, just in time! *Birchas Kohanim* is beginning!!!

YEVARECHECHA HASHEM VEYISHMERECHA!!!
YA'ER HASHEM PANAV EILECHA VICHUNEKA!!!
YISA HASHEM PANAV EILECHA
VEYASEM LECHA SHALOM!!!

Tatty! The Kohanim are saying the Shem Hameforash !!!

That's right, Shimmy, in the Beis Hamikdash the Shem Hameforash, with four letters, is recited!!! Now is the time to say —

"Baruch Hashem Elokei Yisrael Min Ha'Olam V'ad Ha'Olam !"

TOOO---TOOO-TO-TO-TO-TO
TOOO---TOOO-TO-TO-TO-TO
TOOO---TOOO-TO-TO-TO-TO!!!!

Tatty, what are those trumpets??

Those *tekios* announce the arrival of the Kohen who has the water for the *nisuch hamayim*. You can look towards the Shaar Hamayim. Soon, it will be time for *nisuch* of the wine and the water!!!

What is this, Tatty?

Make way!!! Make way!!!

Each day long willow branches are brought and stood on the base around the Mizbeach until they reach one amah above it.

TOOO—TO-TO-TO-TO
TOOO—TO-TO-TO-TO
TOOO—TO-TO-TO-TO-TO!!!

Those are the next set of *tekios* that are blown when the Kohanim stand the *aravos* around the Mizbeach.

In another minute, they will finish and we will see how the Kohanim bring the limbs of the *Tamid* from the ramp to the Mizbeach, and then the big moment will be here: the pouring of the wine and the water!!!

Meanwhile, you can see the Leviim on the platform , getting ready to sing the *Shir Shel Yom*.

I'm really looking forward to their beautiful singing.

Absolutely... There is no song in the world that is more beautiful.

Look over there, Shimmy!!! The Kohen with the bowl of water is approaching the Mizbeach, where the Kohen who will pour the wine is waiting for him.

Raise your hands.

The Kohen is pouring the water into the special cup on the Mizbeach, from where it goes down into the deep *shisin*, the openings from the Mizbeach that lead to the ground, into which the wine of the *nesachim* of the *Korban Tamid* are poured by the second Kohen.

TOOO—TO-TO-TO
OO—TO-TO-T
TOO-TO-TO-T
TO
TO
TO!!!

Father in Heaven! I want to be a tzaddik!!! I want to learn Torah with enthusiasm!!! I want to do mitzvos with simchah!!! Help me, Hashem!!

אכן כאדם תמותון וכאחד השרים תפלו. קומה אלקים שפטה הארץ כי אתה תנחל בכל הגויים.

Hashem! Thank you for giving me the merit to be here in the Beis Hamikdash and to listen to the wonderful songs of the Leviim!!!

ANA HASHEM, HOSHIAH NA! ANA HASHEM, HATZLICHAH NA!

Now look: the Kohanim are going to walk around the Mizbeach with the arba minim!!

Why don't we join them, Tatty??

Very simple: someone who is not a Kohen is not allowed to enter the space between the Ulam and the Mizbeach and in order to go around the Mizbeach, they have to pass through that area!

Now we will go daven in the shul on Har Habayis, until Hallel. We will recite Hallel with everyone else when the Korban Mussaf is brought!

And we'll also shake the arba minim?

Yes. We'll take them with us to the Azarah so that we can shake them during Hallel.

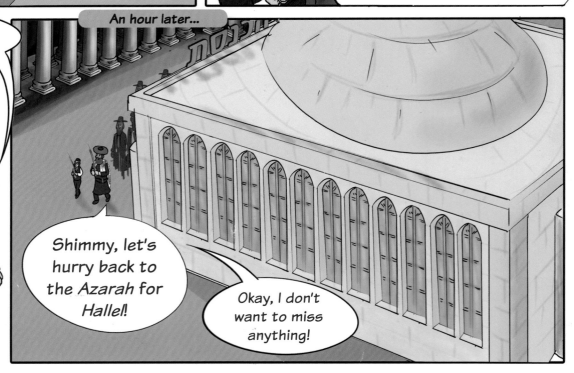

An hour later...

Shimmy, let's hurry back to the Azarah for Hallel!

Okay, I don't want to miss anything!

A few moments later...

Look over there, Shimmy.

The Kohanim are bringing the *Korbanos Mussaf* from the *Lishkas Hakorban* in the *Beis Hamoked*!! You can see the thirteen cows that we bring on the first day of Yom Tov, along with the two rams and the fourteen sheep. The number of the rams and sheep doesn't change the whole Yom Tov, but the number of cows goes down every day...

Right, we learned that in *cheder*!

Tatty, I don't understand...I see lots of Yisraelim going into the *Ezras Hakohanim*!!!

Yisraelim are allowed there during the Shalosh Regalim, as long as they do not go between the *Ulam* and the *Mizbeach*. I am not sure you'll be able to see it from here, but people are even standing on the sides of the *Heichal* and behind the *Kodesh Hakodashim*!

TOOO--TOOO-TO-TO-TO
TOOO--TOOO-TO-TO-TO-TO-TO
TOOO---TOOO-TO-TO-TO-TO-TOI!!!

Oh, *Hallel* is beginning! The Leviim will begin to sing, accompanied by the flutes, and while we recite *Hallel*, the Kohanim will bring the *Korbanos Mussaf*.

HALLELUKAH, HALLELU AVDEI HASHEM, HALLELU ES SHEM HASHEM!!!

BETZEIS YISRAEL MIMITZRAYIM...

HODU L'HASHEM KI TOV KI L'OLAM CHASDO!

HODU L'HASHEM KI TOV KI L'OLAM CHASDO!

A few minutes later...

Tatty, it's so exciting!!! I don't remember ever being this excited...

That's right. Reciting Hallel in the Beis Hamikdash is one of the most uplifting moments ever!!!

Now look at the Kohanim pouring the nesachim of the Korbanos Mussaf. The Leviim are about to sing again.

למנצח בנגינת מזמור לאסף שיר. נודע ביהודה אלקים בישראל גדול שמו. ויהי בשלם סוכו ומעונתו בציון. נדרו ושלמו לה' אלקיכם כל סביביו יבילו שי למורא. יבצר רוח נגידים נורא למלכי ארץ.

TOOO-TO-TO-TO TOOO-TO-TO-TO TOOO-TO-TO-TO TO

I could stand here for hours listening to the Leviim sing...I'm even ready to stand here for the rest of my life!!! I don't need to eat or drink or sleep...It's so sweet and beautiful!!!

I agree, but now we need to go to Har Habayis to bring our korbanos. Then we'll hurry home so Mommy can prepare the seudah from the shelamim meat. Don't forget that we have to eat all the meat from the shelamim by shkiyah tomorrow.

That won't be a problem Tatty...We have lots of guests!

Right, but our guests also need to finish eating their own meat in time. We don't want any to be "nosar."

Wow...so how are we going to do it???

B'ezras Hashem, we'll eat mostly meat and be happy that we are able to eat at the Table of our Father in Heaven.

Tatty, I have a question...

Yes?

How many people are here now?

I don't know for sure, but at least a few million...

And each of them has a korban?

I think that most of them brought *korbanos* to sacrifice today, and the majority brought more than one *korban*...

So how can it be that so many people and so many animals fit in the *Beis Hamikdash*???

Oh, that's an excellent question, and I'll even add to it since many of the people who bought *korbanos* today also brought their *nesachim*....meaning that tens of thousands of tons of flour and upon thousands of gallons of wine are also being brought!

That only makes my question bigger, Tatty!!

That's right, and the answer is the same. It's simply a miracle!

Besides, Shimmy, did you wonder how the Kohanim have time to *shecht* all these *korbanos*, and to skin them and do some other tasks that need to be done to bring the *korban*? How are they all able to spray the blood on the same two corners of the *Mizbeach* in just a few hours? If you do the math, you'll see that every minute between now and when the evening *Korban Tamid* is brought — the Kohanim *shecht* and spray the blood of tens of thousands of *korbanos*!!!

EVERY MINUTE???

Yes! Every minute! If, let's say, there are nearly 10 million *korbanos* in the *Azarah* that need to be brought over seven hours, which equals 420 minutes, then the Kohanim are shechting about 23,809 *karbanos* each minute!

It's unbelievable, Tatty!!!

Of course—it's a MIRACLE!!!

Here are our *korbanos*. We left them tied to pillar number 27684! I made sure to memorize the number...

So where are we going now? Are we going to walk through the *Azarah* with all these *korbanos*?

No Shimmy, we'll go straight into the *Azarah* through the *Shaar Hakorban* on the north, and there the Kohanim will accept the *korbanos* from us. As usual I will place my hands and perform *semichah* on my *korbanos* and then they will be slaughtered by the Kohanim who work very quickly. Later, the Kohanim will bring me the internal organs of the *Korban Shelamim* and the *chazeh* and *shok*, and I will wave them together with the Kohen, and then I'll receive the meat and we can head home...

A few minutes later...

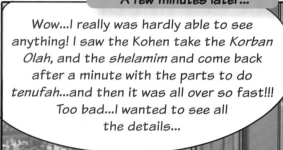

A short time later...

That's actually a good idea...We haven't eaten anything for hours!!!

There are such *tzaddikim* in Yerushalayim!!!

Of course...This is a tradition going back years! There are *baalei chesed* who always offer kiddush and cake and drinks to people returning from the Beis Hamikdash.

Three hours later...

This is a *mechayah*...But we must be on our way. It's getting late!

Absolutely! Let's hurry... and don't forget to thank our host on the way out.

VESAMACHTA BECHAGECHA VEHAYISA ACH SAMEACH!!!

Baruch Atah....asher kidshanu bemitzvosav vetzivanu al achilas shelamim!.

Amen!

A few hours later...

Baruch Atah...Hamavdil Bein Kodesh Lechol!!!

Amen!!!

Tatty, when are we going to simchas beis hasho'evah???

As soon as everyone is ready.

I'll be ready in one minute, Tatty.

Yes, but you're not quite everyone...

A short time later...

Baruch Hashem we got ready really fast...

Tatty! Where is that light from? The streetlights are never so bright!

That's a special light from the Beis Hamikdash, from those tall lamps that we saw. If they've already lit the lamps it means the simchah will be starting any minute...

Amazing!

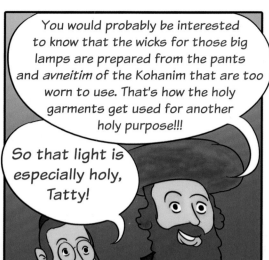

You would probably be interested to know that the wicks for those big lamps are prepared from the pants and avneitim of the Kohanim that are too worn to use. That's how the holy garments get used for another holy purpose!!!

So that light is especially holy, Tatty!

That's right.

Come, let's hurry to the light rail station...Although there is more service now to the Beis Hamikdash and the trains will run all night, we'd better try to beat the crowds if we can...

For sure!

Oh, no, look what's going on here! And that's before the rush!

Exactly...imagine what it will be like during the peak hours!!!

But don't worry... There should be one train every minute, at least...

It's okay... we should always be crowded for simchos!

A few moments later...

I think we'll be able to get onto this train already...

I hope so...

A minute later...

It's so crowded, but I don't mind!! The main thing is that we're on the way to the simchas beis hasho'evah at the Beis Hamikdash!!

That's right...People once used to walk this whole route.

I heard that even today there are people who prefer to do aliyas haregel – b'regel – by walking there. Maybe they want the "sechar halicha."

But with the whole family, it's not practical.

A short time later...

What beautiful music!!!

Look at this light!!!

You can literally feel the *simchah* in the air!!!

It's not just *simchah*...It's the *simchas beis hasho'evah*, and *ruach hakodesh* is also drawn from this!

Let's get closer to the Beis Hamikdash!!

We'll leave our things in the lockers, as usual.

Of course!

And after we enter Har Habayis the women will continue towards the gates leading to their special balconies while the men will continue to the *Ezras Nashim*, where the *simchah* is taking place.

I feel like I'm being pulled by the *simchah* and I don't even have to walk with my feet...!

VESAMACHT...

Har HaBayis is forbidden with shoes, bags, cell phones, cameras, weapons and other such items! All items must be must be stored in the lockers.

True. When the heart yearns for something, the legs carry themselves...

I can't wait to start dancing!!!

Uhmmm...Shimmy, we don't dance at the *simchas beis hasho'evah*...

We don't? Why not? I'm a really good dancer!

You certainly are, Shimmy, but at the *simchas beis hasho'evah*, the *Gedolei Hador* dance, and we have the privilege of looking at them and absorbing their holiness!

Oh...that's very good, even better than dancing...

A few moments later...

What an orchestra!

That's right—the best symphony in the whole world!

And just wait till you see the *Leviim* on the stairs of the *Azarah* with their instruments!

The great moment has arrived...We're entering the Ezras Nashim!

What happens if I get lost, Tatty?

Don't worry, you can always go back towards the Chuldah Gates, and right outside the gate, there is a station set up especially for children who have lost their parents.

We must be some of the first ones here...I see there's still room to get in...

Oh, Shimmy, that doesn't mean anything. I'm sure there are already millions of Yidden in the *Ezras Nashim*. But it's never crowded in the Beis Hamikdash!

And we'll take part in that miracle too?

Yes indeed. Here we go!

Wow! It's incredible! What an orchestra!!

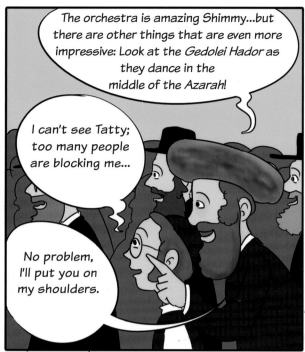

The orchestra is amazing Shimmy...but there are other things that are even more impressive: Look at the *Gedolei Hador* as they dance in the middle of the *Azarah*!

I can't see Tatty; too many people are blocking me...

No problem, I'll put you on my shoulders.

It's so exciting, Tatty! And I don't even know who these *tzaddikim* are...

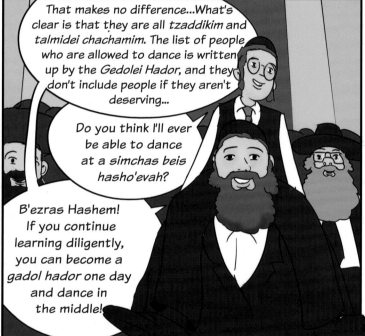

That makes no difference...What's clear is that they are all *tzaddikim* and *talmidei chachamim*. The list of people who are allowed to dance is written up by the *Gedolei Hador*, and they don't include people if they aren't deserving...

Do you think I'll ever be able to dance at a *simchas beis hasho'evah*?

B'ezras Hashem! If you continue learning diligently, you can become a *gadol hador* one day and dance in the middle!

IF I AM HERE, EVERYTHING IS HERE! IF I AM NOT HERE, WHO IS HERE? MY FEET LEAD ME TO THE PLACE THAT I LOVE!!! IF YOU COME TO MY HOUSE — I WILL COME TO YOUR HOUSE, IF YOU DON'T COME TO MY HOUSE, I WON'T COME TO YOUR HOUSE!

I don't recognize these songs, Tatty.

That's because they are special for the *simchas beis hasho'evah*! Hillel Hazaken would sing them in his time, and since then, Yidden throughout the generations sing them. The songs describe Hashem's love for Am Yisrael, and remind us that the holiness of the Beis Hamikdash is dependent on the Shechinah dwelling in this holy place!

PRAISED IS HE WHO HAS NEVER SINNED, AND HE WHO HAS SINNED SHOULD REPENT AND HE WILL BE FORGIVEN! PRAISED IS OUR OLD AGE THAT DID NOT EMBARRASS OUR CHILDHOOD! PRAISED IS OUR OLD AGE THAT ATONED FOR OUR CHILDHOOD!

What are they saying, Tatty?

That depends on who is speaking. The tzaddikim are saying they are happy to be as righteous in their old age as they were in their childhood. But those who stumbled and then returned to the Torah say 'Praised is our old age that atoned for our childhood.' Then together they say: 'Whoever sinned, let him repent and he will be forgiven!'

Shimmy! Look at the Gedolim dancing as they juggle the flaming torches!

Wow!!! How do they do that???

When you have pure kavanos and do things l'shem Shamayim, then everything is possible, Shimmy!

A few hours later...

TOOO-TO-TO-TO TOOO-TO-TO-TO TOOO-TO-TO-TO TOOO-TO-TO-TO-TO

What are these tekios?

They signal that the procession to go draw the water is about to start. Look at the Kohanim with the chatzotzros at the top of the stairs!

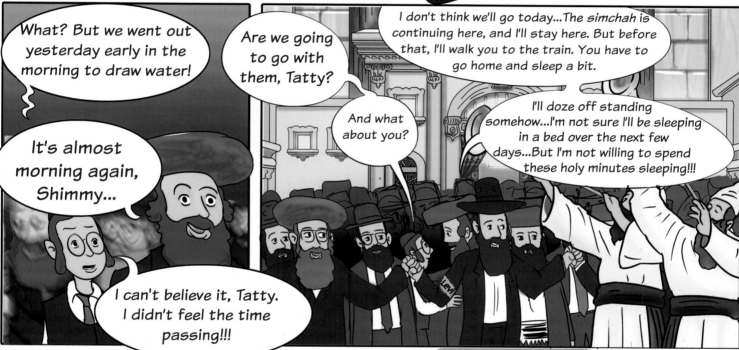

What? But we went out yesterday early in the morning to draw water!

Are we going to go with them, Tatty?

I don't think we'll go today...The simchah is continuing here, and I'll stay here. But before that, I'll walk you to the train. You have to go home and sleep a bit.

It's almost morning again, Shimmy...

And what about you?

I'll doze off standing somehow...I'm not sure I'll be sleeping in a bed over the next few days...But I'm not willing to spend these holy minutes sleeping!!!

I can't believe it, Tatty. I didn't feel the time passing!!!

I really want to stay here with you...But I think you are right...I'm beginning to feel tired, and I want to be able to come back tomorrow night. Is that okay?

Of course! My biggest hope is that you will become a tzaddik and yarei Shamayim! Where else can you get as much Yiras Shamayim as you can get here?

A few hours later...

Shkiyah is in forty minutes. We have to hurry up and finish the meat...

Is there a lot left?

Not too much... I think we'll be able to finish it all.

Good!

I think we will bring our *Shalmei Simchah* tomorrow, and then over the next two days we'll sacrifice your *Shalmei Simchah*, Uncle Avrum. This way we can use them for Shabbos also. On Hoshana Rabbah, we'll bring two sheep for *Shalmei Simchah* from Uncle Shlomo, which we'll eat over Simchas Torah.

Sounds good. This way, it will all be organized...

Right...We'll be able to eat the meat of the *Kodshim* the whole *Yom Tov*, without having any left over!

Of course it's important not to mix the foods together because if, for example the meat of your *Shalmei Simchah* becomes mixed with the meat from our *Shalmei Simchah* two days from now, we'll have to finish everything during the time of your *shelamim*, meaning that very day!

Half an hour later...

Shkiyah is in three minutes...

So am I.

Me too!

I'm finished!

Wonderful...Now we can bentsch and go to the Beis Hamikdash for the *simchas beis hasho'evah*, which began as soon as the evening *Korban Tamid* was brought.

A short time later...

One minute, Tatty. Why are you taking the sheep now? We don't bring *korbanos* at night!

True but right after Shacharis and the *Korban Tamid* I want to offer our *Shalmei Simchah*.

Here...We'll buy tickets for us, and one for the sheep in the animal car!

○ Adult
○ Child

○ Sheep
○ Cow

○ Bicycle

The train is coming, Tatty.

Great...It's not too crowded yet, *baruch Hashem*...We can get on this train.

But first, we have to put the sheep in its place.

Of course!

What a miracle that there's also room for our sheep...

True, and that's exactly how it has to be. The animal car cannot be crowded. Each animal has its own pen, because if the animals are pushed and shoved, they might become damaged and then they won't be able to be used as korbanos!

That would be terrible....

That's right. Especially since the Olei Regel would only find out the animals are *passul* after they arrive here.

Four days later...

Shimmy, today you have to take a long nap!

Why? What's special about today?

Today we'll be going to the Beis Hamikdash for the simchas beis hasho'evah, and you'll be able to stay with me to daven Shacharis tomorrow!

Oh, wow!

How come you're letting me stay for davening tomorrow, Tatty?

First of all, it's the last simchas beis hasho'evah, so tomorrow you'll be able to make up some of the sleep...But what's even more important is that I want you to participate in the chavatah, the beating of the aravos that takes place in the Beis Hamikdash during the nisuch hamayim!

The beating of the aravos? What's that?

The next morning...

Wait and see...

I'm so curious...

I know you are tired Shimmy, but try to stay awake a bit longer... This is the moment you've been waiting for all night!

I'm trying, Tatty!

Look! The Kohanim are starting to give out the aravos from the sides of the Mizbeach to everyone!

Do you think there'll be enough for everybody?

I never heard of anyone who didn't receive an aravah...I guess it's a miracle that there's always enough...

Here, Shimmy...an aravah for me, and for you! Now we'll hit the aravah three times on the floor.

This is the first time I'm doing this mitzvah!

That's right, because it's the first time you're in the Beis Hamikdash on Hoshanah Rabbah!

But how will there be room for everyone to hit their *aravos*? I can't even see the floor...

Don't worry, Shimmy... Just bend down to hit the *aravah* and you'll see what happens...

It's unbelievable...Even though I've seen so many miracles this *Yom Tov*, I still can't get used to them!

That's the way it should be... These miracles are supposed to remind us about the holiness of this place, and of the tremendous love that our Father in Heaven has for us! It would be terrible if we'd get used to them and not notice the message they are sent to give us.

Now we are saying goodbye to Sukkos... Although tomorrow we'll celebrate Shemini Atzeres, it is not part of Sukkos anymore...Its *korbanos* are different and it is considered a *Yom Tov* of its own in several ways...We don't walk around the *Mizbeach* anymore. That's why we will now say goodbye to the *Mizbeach*, which we celebrated joyously around for seven days, and we'll say, 'Yofi Lecha Mizbeach!!! Yofi lecha Mizbeach!!!"

"Yofi Lecha Mizbeach!!! Yofi Lecha Mizbeach!!!"

Tatty, I can't wait for Sukkos next year!!! It was such a magnificent Yom Tov!!!

B'ezras Hashem, Shimmy, Sukkos will return in exactly another year, minus one week...But until then, there will be many other beautiful *Yamim Tovim*, each special in its own way.

I'm waiting for those too, of course...

I am too. You know Shimmy, you're already a year older and you can really feel the specialness of the holidays. If you want, you can even tell others about it.

Of course. I want to tell everyone. And that's exactly what I'll do...

In Those Days, In Our Times

Page 9

Tatty! I'm so happy that the *leshon zehoris* turned white!

So am I, Shimmy...It's a tremendous *simchah*! It means that Hashem has forgiven us for all our sins this Yom Kippur, and that the *avodah* of the Kohein Gadol was accepted!

Can you imagine, children, what a joy it was to get a clear answer from Shamayim that all our sins had been forgiven? When the *Beis Hamikdash* was standing – we would merit this each and every year! The *lashon zehoris* would turn white, and Am Yisrael knew that their sins were forgiven! We daven that we should merit to have this happen again very soon, in our days, in the third *Beis Hamikdash*!

One of the most emotional moments of the whole year in the *Beis Hamikdash* was when the Kohen Gadol emerged safely from the *Kodesh Hakodashim*. As long as he was in the *Kodesh Hakodashim*, the entire nation stood tensely and waited. Would he emerge safely? Would something happen to him? If he had even the slightest sin – he would not have come out of the *Kodesh Hakodashim* alive! When he did appear at the doorway of the *Ulam*, it was an extremely lofty and exciting moment!

Page 10

Is that why everyone was so happy when they saw him come out of the *Kodesh HaKodashim*?

Exactly!

There were millions of Yidden in Yerushalayim for the Shalosh Regalim. The Gemara relates that one year, 1.2 million *korbanos* Pesach were brought, and there were at least 10 people represented by each *korban*! That did not include children and some of the older people, so it's safe to assume that there were nearly 20 million people in Yerushalayim! Can we imagine how much space was needed for everyone to sleep in Yerushalayim? Don't forget all the millions of animals for the various *korbanos* that were also in Yerushalayim... There's no doubt it was one of the miracles performed in Yerushalayim: the city simply expanded and contracted so that it could contain all of its children who came to perform the mitzvah of *aliya l'regel*!

Of course there will be lots of guests... But you must have forgotten that no one ever complained that they didn't have enough room in Yerushalayim...Everyone will fit into the sukkah comfortably, so don't worry about it!

Page 11

Look, Shimmy. Now do you understand better?

These balconies are placed on stone stakes that stick out of the walls of the Ezras Nashim, and the women can stand on these stairs and see the *simchas beis hasho'evah* without anyone else seeing them.

Page 15

Can we watch how they put these balconies into place?

Can you imagine, dear children, what kind of holiness pervaded the *Beis Hamikdash* during the *simchas beis hasho'evah*? Chazal teach us that the people would reach the level of *ruach hakodesh* from this joy!!! Still, it was so important to maintain *tzniyus* standards that they added a special addition to the *Beis Hamikdash* in order to separate the men from the women, despite the fact that it was usually forbidden to make any changes to the structure of the *Beis Hamikdash*. If so, we can certainly learn from that how important it is in our day to maintain *tzniyus* standards, especially since we do not have the protective merit of the special holiness of the *Beis Hamikdash*...

In Those Days, In Our Times

In order to understand how high these lamps that illuminated the Beis Hamikdash during the simchas beis hasho'evah were, imagine a building that is ten floors high... Yes! These lamps were as tall as a ten-story building, but they weren't as wide as a building. They were very narrow and tall...Can you imagine how scary it was to climb them? When we climb a regular ladder, we're afraid... So what can we say about a ladder as tall as a ten-story building? Remember, the young Kohanim did not climb up the ladders empty-handed...They had big, heavy pitchers full of oil on their backs!!! This was no simple task, but the young Kohanim were so excited to have the merit of illuminating the courtyard of the King of Kings—that they barely noticed how hard it was!

Page 17

Wow!!

I hope that there are sheep left for us...

Of course there are. The dealers here know that demand goes up and they prepare accordingly. Look at all those trucks full of sheep and cows waiting to be unloaded!

Page 18

Think, children, how many korbanos needed to be purchased in Yerushalayim before each one of the Shalosh Regalim: Let's assume, as we wrote earlier, that there were 10 million people in Yerushalayim...Let's say that each one of them had only two korbanos — the ones that each person is obligated to bring on each Regel: Olas Re'iyah and Shalmei Chagigah...We've already reached 20 million animals for korbanos!!! But don't forget that there were millions more animals that the olei regel brought as nedarim and nedavos!!! And don't forget that many of the olei regel also brought as many Shalmei Simchah as they needed for meat!!! There's no doubt that millions of animals were needed to supply the korbanos for the olei regel!!! Most of these korbanos were purchased by olei regel in Yerushalayim...So can you imagine how huge this animal market was?

The mitzvah of nisuach hamayim was a halachah l'Moshe mi'Sinai, according to most opinions. But still, it is important to know that it contains a tremendous brachah for Am Yisrael: In the merit of this mitzvah, the rains of the coming year are blessed! Let's think about it: Our Father in Heaven wants so much to do good for us that He gives us a special mitzvah in whose merit He can bless us...Do you understand how much love for us Hashem conveys through this mitzvah?

Page 31

NISHMAS KOL CHAI TEVARECH ES SHIMCHA HASHEM ELOKEINU !!!

Of course. I wasn't planning to let go for a second...I don't even know the way home!

Page 32

Tatty, where is the mitzvah of nisuch hamayim written in the Torah?

It's not. It was given to Moshe at Har Sinai, orally. It's called "halachah l'Moshe miSinai." That's why the Tzedokim, who lived in the days of the Mishnah, did not believe in this mitzvah — because they didn't believe in Torah Sheba'al Peh. They were kofrim, heretics!

Exactly...Unfortunately, one year there was a Tzedoki Kohen and no one knew about it. He poured the water over his feet instead of into the special vessel for this purpose in the Beis Hamikdash...

What reshaim!

Oh, my!!!

There was a lot of highly publicized activity regarding the filling of the water from the Shiloach Spring. First, they filled the water for the nisuch hamayim specifically from the Shiloach Spring, and not from the water of the kiyor, for example...Aside for that, apparently there were many tekiyos at the time when they went out to fill the water, when they returned and during all of the activity connected to the water...Chazal explain (Yerushalmi, Succah Perek 4, halachah 6, and see Piskei Hari"d and the commentaries on the Yerushalmi) that the reason for that was specifically because the Tzedokim questioned the mitzvah of nisuch hamayim and did not acknowledge it. That is why so much effort was made to publicize the mitzvah as much as possible, in order to declare that we do not agree with the heretical ways of the Tzedokim!

In Those Days, In Our Times

Each day of Sukkos, they would go down to a place near Yerushalayim called Motza, and they would bring willow branches from there that were 11 amos long, which they would stand up on the foundation that surrounded the Mizbeach, in a way that they were an amah taller than the Mizbeach, and leaned over it (Succah 45a). Some opinions hold that the Kohanim would surround the Mizbeach each day with the willow leaves. In addition to this mitzvah of the aravah, which is a halachah l'Moshe mi'Sinai – they would beat the aravos on the seventh day of Sukkos, according to the custom of the Neviim. But we will discuss that mitzvah further on.

It is also worth mentioning (Bartenura on Mishnayos) that the place where the aravos was taken from was called Motza, because it was "mutza", taken out, and exempt from the king's taxes. That means that the residents of the town did not have to pay taxes to the kingdom, because it was such an important place—it was the source for the aravos which were taken for this mitzvah in the Beis Hamikdash!

The mitzvah of nisuch hamayim was performed together with the pouring of the wine of the Korban Tamid. Near the southwestern corner of the Mizbeach were two basins, one for the wine of nisuch hayayin and one for the water of nisuch hamayim. The eastern basin was for the wine, while the western one was for the water. The basin of the wine had a thicker hole than the one for the water because wine is thicker and flows more slowly, and the objective was that the wine and the water should finish flowing out of the basins at the same time, and should together continue into the deep shisin (crevices) under the Mizbeach.

The Kohen is pouring the water into the special cup on the Mizbeach, from where it goes down into the deep shisin, the openings from the Mizbeach that lead to the ground, into which the wine of the nesachim of the Korban Tamid are poured by the second Kohen.

Page 36

Page 36

Think about it: On a Yom Tov of the Shalosh Regalim, millions of people brought millions of korbanos! A large part of these korbanos were shelamim, which needed to be eaten on the day they were sacrificed or the next day until shkiyah. In other words: the korbanos had to be offered, and then taken home, where the meat had to be koshered and cooked, and then eaten, all in two days! Still, they usually managed to do it... Apparently, when you realize what a zechus it is to eat from the Table of the King, everything is possible!

One of the most amazing miracles in the Beis Hamikdash occurred mostly during the Shalosh Regalim, when there was tremendous crowding in the Azarah. The Gemara relates that the Azarah was packed to capacity, and even the area north and south of the Heichal was crowded with people, as was the area behind, and west of the Kodesh Hakodashim. It was so packed that even if someone wanted to fall, he couldn't, because there were too many people around him...People lost their footing on the ground and were literally suspended in the air!

If it was so crowded, how was it possible to bow down in the Azarah? Bear in mind that in order to bow, they all had to come to the east side of the Azarah so that they could bow westwards, towards the Heichal. In other words, the many people who were in the Azarah had to pack into an even smaller area on the eastern side of the Azarah—and then bow down! But a great miracle happened here. Not only did they all manage to bow, but each person had four amos, four cubits of space so that he could admit to his sins while bowing without anyone hearing him. The Azarah "simply" stretched to several times its usual size!

Page 37

Page 43

In Those Days, In Our Times

It was amazing! All of Yerushalayim was illuminated by the lamps of the *Beis Hamikdash*, to the extent that Chazal tell us (*Succah* 53a) that a woman could check wheat anywhere in Yerushalayim by the light of the *simchas beis hasho'evah*! It's hard to know if it was natural light, or if it miraculously illuminated the whole city, but one thing is clear: the absolutely wondrous scene, in which all of Yerushalayim was illuminated and glowing from the light of the *Beis Hamikdash*, was something that cannot be described! Let's hope we merit seeing that in our time!

Not everyone was able to dance at the *simchas beis hasho'evah* in the *Beis Hamikdash*...Only *tzaddikim* and people of stature, *gedolei hador*, who were able to dance completely *l'shem Shamayim*, in honor of the King of Kings, were permitted to dance. Everyone else stood around them and observed their actions, drawing in the holiness and spiritual feelings! Can you imagine the scene of all the *Gedolei Yisrael* dancing together in holiness and purity? It was absolutely amazing!!!

Page 45

I can't wait to start dancing!!!

Page 44

Baruch Hashem we got ready really fast...

Tatty! Where is that light from? The streetlights are never so bright!

That's a special light from the *Beis Hamikdash*, from those tall lamps that we saw. If they've already lit the lamps it means the *simchah* will be starting any minute...

Amazing!

Can we possibly understand what "*ruach hakodesh*" is? Of course not...But we know that it is a very high level that only very great tzaddikim merit to reach! And yet, one could draw *ruach hakodesh* from the *simchas beis hasho'evah*; the holiness was so intense in the *Beis Hamikdash* during the *simchas beis hasho'evah* that it was much easier to reach high spiritual levels! Chazal tell us that the Navi Yona, whom we have all heard of, first said *nevuah* after participating in the *simchas beis hasho'evah* in the *Beis Hamikdash*; that was from where he drew the special holiness needed to sanctify himself in order to merit *nevuah*!

You've surely been at a wedding, right? How many players did the orchestra have? One? Two? Maybe even seven? There are orchestras around the world that have hundreds of players, but there is none that begins to get even close to the amazing orchestra of the *Leviim*, who would stand with unusual instruments on the stairs of the *Azarah* playing with great longing for Hashem, with such *kedushah*! We can't even imagine how sublime it was...How we long to see and hear this too!

Page 45

Page 46

Wow! It's incredible! What an orchestra!!

What beautiful music!!!

Look at this light!!!

You can literally feel the *simchah* in the air!!!

It's not just *simchah*...It's the *simchas beis hasho'evah*, and *ruach hakodesh* is also drawn from this!

Let's get closer to the *Beis Hamikdash*!!

In Those Days, In Our Times

Page 47

Yes children!!! Each and every one of you can be a *gadol hador*, if you just learn with great diligence and *hasmadah*! Sometimes, we hear about great *tzaddikim* and we feel so small compared to them that we are sure we can never be like them...But that's a big mistake!! Each one of you can be the next *gadol hador*, if you make the effort.

Page 46

That makes no difference...What's clear is that they are all *tzaddikim* and *talmidei chachamim*. The list of people who are allowed to dance is written up by the *Gedolei Hador*, and they don't include people if they aren't deserving...

Do you think I'll ever be able to dance at a *simchas beis hasho'evah*?

B'ezras Hashem! If you continue learning diligently, you can become a *gadol hador* one day and dance in the middle!

We might think, *chalilah*, that it is not respectful for the *gedolei hador* to stand and dance with torches as jugglers do today...But we have to remember before Whom these *tzaddikim* were dancing! They were dancing before the King of Kings, HaKadosh Baruch Hu — in His Home, the Beis Hamikdash!!! When it is a dance for the King of Kings there is no need to worry that it is not dignified enough — on the contrary — it is a tremendous privilege and *zechus*!!!

In the *Beis Hamikdash*, all kinds of miracles were constantly happening... They happened for an important reason! These miracles reminded us that the *Beis Hamikdash* was the Palace of the King of Kings, and that there were no rules of nature there...Everything that happened in the *Beis Hamikdash* was miraculous! See you there soon b'ezras Hashem!

Page 47

A few hours later...

Shkiyah is in forty minutes. We have to hurry up and finish the meat...

Is there a lot left?

Not too much... I think we'll be able to finish it all.

Good!

Page 50

It's unbelievable...Even though I've seen so many miracles this Yom Tov, I still can't get used to them!

Imagine that the king would invite you to the palace for a whole week...How would you feel? Could you possibly be luckier??? That's exactly what we would have if the Beis Hamikdash was still standing! For the entire week of Sukkos, we were the guests of the King of Kings. We rejoiced in His Home, spent time there, and even ate at His Table — from the various *korbanos* of the holiday! No other invitation is as special as that!

GLOSSARY

Aliyah l'regel: holiday pilgrimage

Amos: (plural of *amah*) "forearm" length – meaning, the distance between the elbow and the tip of the big finger (bet. 1.5-2 feet per *amah*)

Arba minim: four species used on Sukkos

Avneitim: belts worn by Kohanim

Avodas hatamid: service of bringing the daily sacrifice

Azarah: Temple courtyard

Bedieved: less preferable halachically but if you already did it that way you do not need to repeat the mitzvah

Beis Hamoked: One of the chambers which had a fire which the Kohanim used to warm themselves or cook food

Chatzotzros: trumpets

Chazeh: the chest of an animal

Chuldah Gates: Named after Chuldah the Prophetess

Deshen: ashes

Duchanim: place where Leviim or Kohanim stand and bless the people or sing and play instruments

Ezras Nashim: literally, the women's section – a permanent section of the Beis Hamikdash that women use, except during the *simchas beis hasho'evah*, thereby necessitating a second temporary *Ezras Nashim* balcony to be built each year

Har Habayis: Temple Mount

Heichal Hashem or Heichal: the Holy Temple / outer part of the actual Beis Hamikdash (Temple) building

Kavanos: (proper) intentions

Ketores: incense offering, a sacrifice offered twice daily, consisting of eleven types of spices plus lye, wine, salt and a small amount of an herb that produces smoke

Kodesh Hakodashim: Holy of Holies – the holiest place in the Beis Hamikdash

Kodshim: a general term for animals set aside to be used as sacrifices

Kohen Gadol: High Priest, a Kohen who is designated to be more holy and is entrusted with special responsibilities not given to any other Kohen

Korban Chagigah: see *Shalmei Chagigah*

Korban Olah: see *Olas Hare'iyah*

Korbanos: sacrifices

Korbanos nedarim: vow sacrifices; owner is liable for its loss, meaning if he loses the animal before it is sacrificed he must buy another one.

Korbanos nedavos: vow sacrifices; owner is not liable for its loss, meaning if he loses the animal before it is sacrificed, he does not have to buy another one

Korbanos shelamim: see *Shelamim*

Lashon shel zehoris: a special red-colored dyed wool string tied to the Beis Hamikdash and the goat sent to "*azazel*" (the barren cliff from which the goat was thrown down)

Lechatchilah: ideally / halachically preferable

Lishkas Hagazis: literally Chamber of Hewn Stone; Meeting place of the Sanhedrin — High Court and also a place where the Kohanim daven and hold three of the lotteries that determine which Kohen will perform the *avodah*

Lishkas Hakorban: literally Chamber of Sacrifice

Lishkas Hanezirim: literally Chamber of Nazirs

Lug: Liquid measurement; approximately 20 ounces.

Midrashim: rabbinical explanations of the Torah

Minchas Hachavisin: flour and oil offering

Minchas Hatamid: daily flour offering

Nikanor Gates: beautiful copper and bronze-covered doors of one of the Temple gates. Donated by an Egyptian Jew named Nikanor.

Nesachim: wine libations (plural), meaning pouring of wine on the altar into the attached funnel done during almost all *korbanos*.

Nisuch hamayim: water libation service performed during Sukkos. Water is poured into one of the funnels attached to the altar.

Nisuch hayayin: wine libation (singular)

Nosar: Leftover meat that was not consumed in time and is therefore forbidden to be eaten.

Olah (singular), *Olos* (plural): sacrifices entirely burned on the altar

Olas hare'iyah: a type of *Olah*, brought specifically when coming to the Temple on the Three Festivals.

Oleh regel: holiday pilgrim – a Yid who is going up to Yerushalayim to bring sacrifices at the Beis Hamikdash on Pesach, Sukkos or Shavuos ("The Three Festivals")

Re'iyah: the mitzvah of making an appearance at the Beis Hamikdash on the Three Festivals

Sechar halicha: The reward for the (extra) toil of walking to do a mitzvah.

Semichah: resting hands on the animal (accompanied by confession)

Shaar hakorban: gate through which some sacrifices were brought into the Temple

Shalmei Chagigah: a type of *Shelamim*, brought specifically on the Shalosh Regalim

Shalmei Simchah: a type of *Shelamim*, brought specifically on the Shalosh Regalim

Shalosh Regalim: the three holidays for which every Jewish male over bar mitzvah is obligated to go to Yerushayalim to bring sacrifices, so long as he is physically able.

Shelamim: sacrifices, parts of which are burned on the altar, other parts of which are eaten by the owner and by all the Kohanim whose "family" (work group members) is on call that day. This is according to the opinion of the Rambam.

Shem Hameforash: the explicit Divine Name that only the Kohen Gadol is permitted to say on Yom Kippor

Shir Shel Yom: daily chapter of Tehillim (Psalms)

Shok: thigh (middle part of animal's leg)

Simchas beis hasho'evah: celebration of the drawing of the water during the Sukkos holiday (held every day of *chol hamoed* except for Shabbos)

Tamid: daily sacrifice of a one-year-old male sheep

Tamim: unblemished – meaning animals that do not have defects such as: broken bones, legs that are not the same length, or missing eyes

Tenufah: "Waiving of the"

Terumas hadeshen: removal of ashes from altar

Tzedoki (singular) *Tzedokim* (plural): followers of Tzaddok who deny the Oral Torah

Ulam: entrance chamber of the Temple

Sources

Page 9
Leshon zehoris
"A *leshon zehoris* [a string woven from wool and dyed red] was tied to the entrance of the *heichal,* and when the goat came to the desert, the string would turn white, as it says: If your sins will be red, they will turn white as snow." (*Mishnayos Yoma*, 6:48)

Kohanim Gedolim during the Second *Beis Hamikdash*
"Rabba bar Bar Chana and Rabi Yochanan said: Where does it say that Fear of Hashem will add days and that the years of the evil will be shortened? Fear of Hashem will add days – that is the first *Beis Hamikdash*, which stood for 410 years, and only 18 *kohanim gedolim* served there, and the years of the evil will be cut short – that is the second *Mikdash* which stood for 420 years, and more than 300 *kohanim* [*gedolim*] served in it. Subtract the 40 years that Shimon Hatzaddik served, and the 80 years that Yochanan Kohen Gadol served, and the 10 years of Yishmael ben Fabi, and the 11 that Rabi Elazar ben Charsom served, calculate: each of the others did not live out the year." (*Yoma*, 9a: see *Yerushalmi, Yoma* 1:1)

Page 10
The Kohen Gadol upon emerging from the *Kodesh Hakodashim*
"And they accompanied him to his home. And he would make a Yom Tov for his beloved ones when he emerged safely from the *Kodesh*." (*Mishnayos Yoma*, 7:4)
"*Emes mah nehedar*, how beautiful it was to see the Kohen Gadol when he emerged from the *Kodesh Kadashim* unharmed." (*Mussaf* of Yom Kippur)

Building a Sukkah on Motzaei Yom Kippur–
"The ones who are diligent with mitzvos begin to build the sukkah right away on Motzaei Yom Kippur so as to go from one mitzvah to another." (*Shulchan Aruch, Orach Chaim* 624:5)

Page 11
Place in Yerushalayim
"No one ever said to his friend, there is not enough room for me to sleep in Yerushalayim." (*Mishnayos Avos* 5:5)

Simchas beis hasho'evah
"They said, anyone who has not seen a *simchas beis hasho'evah* has not seen joy in his life." (*Mishnayos Sukkah* 5:1)

All night long
"Rabi Yehoshua ben Chananya said: When we would rejoice at the *simchas beis hasho'evah*, we did not see sleep in our eyes. How? The first hour – was the *Tamid* of the morning, from there – to *davening*, from there – to the *Korban Mussaf*, from there – to *Tefillas Mussaf*, from there – to the *Beis Medrash*, from there – to eat and drink, from there – to *daven Minchah*, from there – to the *Tamid* of the evening, and from there on to the *simchas beis hasho'evah*." (*Sukkah*, 53a)

Page 14
The repair in the Ezras Nashim
"On Motzaei Yom Tov Rishon, they went down to the Ezras Nashim and did a big *tikkun,* repair, there." (*Sukkah* 51a). "What is this *tikkun*? Rabi Elazar said, as we learned: originally it was level, and then they built a gallery balcony. The women were seated above and the men, below. " (*Sukkah* 51b).
"And they surrounded it with a balcony: How did they do that? They drove stakes into the walls, protruding from all around the walls, and each year, they arranged the balconies around them, so that the women could stand there during the *simchas beis hasho'evah* and be able to see. That was the big *tikkun* that the *Mishnah* says was carried out each year."

When was the *Ezras Nashim* prepared
Although from the *Mishnah* it could be understood that they did this on Motzaei Yom Tov, the Rambam writes (Chapter 8, *Hilchos Lulav* 12): "On *Erev Yom Tov Rishon* they would affix in the *Mikdash* a place for women above and men below so that they should not mix with one another." It makes sense that they did this before Yom Tov because it is hard to believe that they had time to make the change just on Motzaei Yom Tov. We must say that the intention of the Gemara is that the separation of men and women took place on Motzaei Yom Tov, even though the physical work was done before Yom Tov."

Entering the Ezras Nashim through special gates
(Tavnis Heichal)

Prohibition of altering the structure of the Beis Hamikdash
See *Sukkah* 51b; *Eiruvin* 104a and more. Chazal derived this from the *passuk* (*Divrei Hayamim* I, 28:19): "All was in writing, from the Hand of Hashem, which He gave me to understand, all the works of the pattern."

Page 15
Structure of the balconies
"Out of fear that perhaps men and women would mix, they surrounded it with opaque glass, and made such stairs so that the women could stand there and look at the Jews entering the *simchas beis hasho'evah* there." (*Rambam Peirush Hamishnayos Middos* 2:5)

Awe of the *Mikdash* and prohibition of bringing in mundane items
"It is a *mitzvas aseh* to be in awe of the *Mikdash*, as it says, "*Umikdashi tira'u*." You are not afraid of the *Mikdash*, but of the One who commanded that we fear it. What is this fear? A person should not enter Har Habayis with his stick or with his shoes or his undergarment with pockets to carry things, or with the dust on his feet or his coins bundled in his handkerchief."

Page 16
The lamps at the *simchas beis hasho'evah*
"There were lamps of gold, and four golden vessels at their head, and four ladders for each one of them, and four young men from the *pirchei kehunah* holding pitchers of 120 *lug*, which they poured into each vessel. From the worn pants of the Kohanim and from the belts, they would make wicks and would light them. There wasn't a courtyard in Yerushalayim that was not illuminated by the light of the *sho'evah*." (*Sukkah* 51a). "*Tanna*, we learn from a *braisa*: The height of the lamp was fifty cubits." (*Sukkah*, 52b).

The miracle that the lamps stood
"Bar Kappara said: the height is one hundred cubits. The Yerushalmi asks, we have learned that anything that stands one hundred cubits high needs a base of 33 cubits wide. But if each of the four lamps would have had a base of 33 plus a ladder on each side – the entire *Azarah* was just one hundred and eighty seven cubits long and one hundred thirty five cubits wide! It must mean then the space the bases occupied was miraculous." (*Yerushalmi Sukkah* 5:2; and see *Korban Ha'eidah*).

The number of lamps at the *simchas beis hasho'evah*
(*Baal Haturim, Badmibar* 8:7.)

Page 17
Pirchei kehunah filled the lamps with oil
"Four lads from the *pirchei kehunah* holding oil flasks of 120 *lug*. The question was asked: is it 120 for all the vessels, or did each vessel hold 120 *lug*? Come and hear: And in their hands were flasks of oil of 30 *lug*, and together it amounted to 120 *lug*.

It says: They were even better than the son of Marta bas Baisos. It was said of the son of Marta bas Baisos that he would take two large thighs of a big ox that was purchased for 1000 *zuz*, and would walk slowly but his fellow Kohanim did not let him do so because of "*berov am hadras Melech*." They did not allow him to walk on his own because it is a greater honor for the King when many people do an action together.

What does it mean that they were better? Does it refer to the weight? But the thighs of the ox are heavier than 30 *lug*. It refers to the incline. The son of Marta walked up the ramp that wasn't so steep, while they climbed the ladders that were much straighter." (*Sukkah* 52b)

Page 20
Olas Re'iyah for one under bar mitzvah
See *Rashi* and *Tosafos Chagigah* 2a; *Rambam, Hilchos Chagigah,* 2:3; and the *Lechem Mishneh* and *Mishneh L'Melech ibid*. It is clear that a child is not obligated to bring *Olas Re'iyah* [and the same likely applies to *Shalmei Chagigah*], but the question is if the father is obligated to bring an *Olas Nedavah* [a voluntary *korban*] for the child, and even on that, most of the Rishonim are of the opinion that there is no such obligation.

Page 23
When was the preferred time to bring the *Olas Re'iyah* and *Shalmei Chagigah*–
"It is a mitzvah to be early and bring it on the first day. If he did not bring it on the first day, whether intentionally or by accident – he should do it on the second day, and whoever brings it late is repugnant…' (*Rambam, Hilchos Chagigah* 1:5)

Page 30
Order of the procession to fill the water
"And two Kohanim stood in the upper gate that descends from the *Ezras Yisrael* to the *Ezras Nashim*, with two trumpets in their hands. The *gever* calls, blows a *tekiah*, a *teruah* and a *teikah*. They reached the tenth step, they blew a *tekiah*, a *teruah* and a *tekiah*. They reached the *Azarah*, they blew a *tekiah*, a *teruah* and a *tekiah*. They would blow and walk until they reached the gate that went out east. They reached the gate that exits from the east, and they turned to face west and said, our fathers who were in this place turned their backs to the *Heichal Hashem* and their faces to the east, and they would bow towards the east to the sun, and our eyes are turned to Hashem. Rabi Yehudah says, they would repeat and say, We are to Hashem, and to Hashem are our eyes." (*Mishnayos Sukkah* 5:4). The explanation

of the call of the "*gever*" – see Gemara (*Yoma* 20b, and see *Rashi* there): "What is the call of the *gever*? Rav said: a man called, and Rav Sheila said: a rooster called."

The *Meiri* (*Sukkah* 50a): "Two Kohanim stood at the upper gate that descended from the *Ezras Yisrael* to the *Ezras Nashim* with two trumpets in hand. The *gever* called – and it is that same call that is issued near dawn to summon the Kohanim to the *avodah* and the Leviim to *duchan,* and Yisrael to where they should be standing. They blew a *tekiah*, a *teruah* and a *tekiah*, as a sign that they should go fill the vessel for the *nisuch* from the Shiloach etc. When they reached the *Azarah* – meaning: the floor of the *Ezras Nashim,* they blew a *tekiah*, a *teruah* and a *tekiah* another time, and these blasts were longer than the previous ones, until they reached the gate leading from the *Ezras Nashim* to Har Habayis, and descended towards the east. When they emerged, they turned to face west, to the side of the *Azaros* and the *Heichal* and they would say, our fathers who were in this place in the First *Beis Hamikdash* would turn their backs to the *Heichal Hashem* and their faces east, because they served the sun, but we have our eyes to Hashem etc. Afterwards, they would depart from there and go to the water with song and praise and they would fill [the vessels]. And know that they had in mind not to enter the *Mikdash* with the water until daybreak."

Page 32
The amount of water drawn

"A saucer of gold that holds three *lugim* he would fill from the Shiloach." (*Mishnayos Sukkah*, 4:9)

The source of *nisuch hamayim* is a *halachah L'Moshe MiSinai*

"Rabi Assi said Rabi Yochanan said: [The *din* of] Ten trees, *aravah* and *nisuch hamayim* - are all *halachah l'Moshe miSinai*." (*Sukkah* 34a)

The source of the water had to be from a spring

See *Sukkah* 48b: "From where do we know this? Rav Eina said: *Usheavtem mayim besason, mim'aynei hayeshuah.*" The Ritva explains (*ibid*): "Where do we know this from? It appears that the question of the Gemara applies to all the aspects of *nisuch hamayim,* that they needed to pour water on the *Mizbeach,* and that the water should come from the Shiloach, which is a spring, and it should be done with *simchah*. The answer to all these questions is found in the *passuk "Usheavtem mayim…"* They all appear in the *passuk*: water, joy and spring, *mayim, sasson* and *ma'ayan.*"

The story of the Tzedoki who poured the water onto his feet

"And to the one pouring he says raise your hand, because once, one poured the water onto his legs, and the entire nation pelted him with their *esrogim*." (*Sukkah* 48b)

Drawing the water was not done while wearing *bigdei kehunah*

See *Tosafos Sukkah* 50a, *beginning* "*Ve'i*".

Page 33
The Water Gate

"The southern gates were near the west: Shaar Ha'elyon, Shaar Hadelek, Shaar Habechoros and Shaar Hamayim [Water Gate]. Why was it called the Water Gate? Because they would bring the vessel of water for *nisuch* on Sukkos through it." (*Mishnayos Shekalim* 6:3)

Location of the *Mizbeach*
Ezras Kohanim, 1:4.

Terumas Hadeshen

We find in the Mishnah (*Yoma* 1:8): "Each day, they would clean the *deshen*, the ash, off the *Mizbeach* at the call of the *gever* or thereabouts, whether before or after. On Yom Kippur, it happened from *chatzos*, and on the Regalim it happened during the first third of the night." But the reason for this is because on the Regalim it was necessary to clear a large amount of *deshen*, that remained from the *korbanos* of the previous day, so they started earlier. Indeed, Kol Ramaz already commented (in his second response) that this is only on the second day of Sukkos – when there was already a lot of *deshen* on the *Mizbeach* from the day before, while the first day, there was no reason to make the *terumas hadeshen* so early.

It is worth emphasizing that the water for the *nisuch hamayim* – was not brought into the *Azarah* at that time, because if they would have done that – the water would have become unusable because it would have to sit overnight." (See *Tosafos Sukkah* 50a, beginning "*Ve'i*")

Page 34
Description of the *Terumas Hadeshen*

"*Tormin es hamizbeach* – the ash that Kohen would remove with one shovel, whether there was a lot or a little, as long as it was not less than a *kometz* [that is called *Terumas Hadeshen*]. The Kohen puts it on the east side of the ramp and it was absorbed in its place, as it says (*Vayikra* 6) "*V'herim es hadeshen…* and put it near the *Mizbeach…*" And that was the beginning of the *avodah* of the morning, at dawn."

(*Rashi, Yoma* 20a)

"The one in charge said to them, go out and see if the time for slaughtering has come. If so, the one seeing would say, *barkai*. Matisya ben Shmuel says, [the one in charge would ask] is the entire east illuminated until Chevron? And [the one who could see] said, yes." (*Mishnayos Yoma* 3:1)

The morning service
See *Mishnayos Tamid*.

Place where the blood from the *Olah* was thrown
"The *olah, kodshei kodashim*, was slaughtered in the north, and the Kohen received its blood in a *kli shares* in the north, and its blood needed two applications that are really four." (*Mishnayos Zevachim*, 5:4)

Page 35
Order of the prayers of the Kohanim
"The one in charge told them, make one *brachah*, and they recited it, and said the Ten Commandments, *Shema, Vehayah Im Shamoa, Vayomer*, and blessed the nation with the three *brachos* of *Emes, Veyatziv* and *Avodah* and *Birchas Kohanim* and on Shabbos they added one more *brachah* for the outgoing shift of Kohanim." (*Tamid* 32b)

The order of *Birchas Kohanim* in the *Mikdash*
"*Birchas Kohanim*; how did it happen? In the land [not in the *Beis Hamikdash*], they said it in three *brachos*, and in the *Mikdash* in one *brachah*. In the *Mikdash* he says the Name of Hashem as it is written, and in the land, its *kinui*, nickname, is used. In the land, the Kohanim raised their hands parallel to their shoulders and in the *Mikdash*, they raised their hands above their heads, aside for the Kohen Gadol who did not raise his hands higher than the *tzitz*." (*Sotah*, 7:6)

Nusach of replying Amen in the *Mikdash*
"All the *brachos* in the *Mikdash* ended with *Min Ha'Olam*. When the heretics sowed destruction and said there is only one world [no *Olam Haba*], it was established to say "*min ha'olam v'ad ha'olam*." (*Brachos* 9:5)

Tekios at the Water Gate:
"They reached the water gate, and blew a *tekiah, teruah, tekiah*." (*Sukkah* 4:9)

Page 36
The mitzvah of *Aravah*
"How is the mitzvah of *aravah* performed? There was a place below Yerushalayim and it was called Motza. They went down there and collected *morbios*

of *aravah*, and they came and stood them on both sides of the *Mizbeach*, with their heads bending towards the *Mizbeach* on it. They blew a *tekiah, teruah, tekiah*. Each day they would walk around the *Mizbeach* once and said "*Ana Hashem hoshia na, ana Hashem hatzlicha na*." Rabi Yehudah says, "*Ani vehu hoshia na*." That day [Hoshana Rabba] they would circle the *Mizbeach* seven times. When they left, what did they say? "*Yofi lecha Mizbeach, yofi lecha Mizbeach.*". Rabi Eliezer said, "*Le'Kah velach Mizbeach, Le'Kah velach Mizbeach*."

The source for *Mitzvas Aravah* is Halachah L'Moshe MiSinai
"Rabi Assi said Rabi Yochanan said: [The *din* of] Ten trees, *aravah* and *nisuch hamayim* - are all *halachah l'Moshe miSinai*." (*Sukkah* 34a)

How the *Nisuch Hamayim* was done
"*Nisuch Hamayim*, how was it done? a gold vessel that holds three *lugim* was filled from the Shiloach. They came to the Water Gate, and blew a *tekiah, teruah, tekiah*. He went up the ramp and turned to the left; there were two silver cups there. Rabi Yehudah says, they were from plaster, but they were blackened from the wine. And they had holes like small nostrils, one wider and one narrower, so that they should finish at the same time. The western one held water, the eastern one, wine. If he poured water into the hole for the wine, and the wine into the hole for the water, he is *yotzei*. Rabi Yehudah says, he would pour with a vessel that held one *lug* all eight days. And the pourer was told, raise your hands, because one once poured on his legs, and the whole nation pelted him with their *esrogim*." (*Mishnayos Sukkah* 4:9)

Page 37
Shir Shel Yom
"The song that the Leviim said in the *Beis Hamikdash*, on the first day they would say, '*L'Hashem ha'aretz umeloah, tevel veyoshvei vah.*' On the second day they would say, '*Gadol Hashem umehullal me'od be'ir Elokeinu har kodsho.*' On the third day they would say, '*Elokim nitzav b'adas Kel, bekerev Elokim yishpot.*' On the fourth day they would say, '*Kel nekamos Hashem Kel nekamos hofia.*' On the fifth day they would say: '*Harninu l'Elokim uzeinu hariu l'Elokei Yaakov.*' On the sixth day they would say: '*Hashem malach geius lavesh.*' On Shabbos they said, '*Mizmor shir leyom Hashabbos, Mizmor shir l'asid lavo leyom shekulo Shabbos menuchah lechayei olamim.*" (*Mishnayos Tamid*, 7:4)

They stood crowded and bowed with space
"Rav Yehudah said, Rav said: When Yisrael were *oleh regel* they were crowded when they stood together, but when they bowed there was plenty of space and the crowd spread as far as eleven cubits behind the *Beis Hakapores*. What does this mean? Even though [the crowd was so large] that they spread eleven cubits behind *Beis Hakapores,* because it was so tightly packed, when they bowed, they had space, and that is one of the ten miracles that occurred in the *Mikdash*." (*Yoma* 21a)

"*Tzefufim*, crowded, comes from the language of *tzaf*; people were so crowded one against the other, that they had no place to bend to this side or that, and they stood straight as a beam, and their legs were lifted above the ground. They would bow with space – when they fell in a bow, a miracle happened and the place expanded until there were four *amos* between them, so no one should hear his friend's admittance of his sins, and they should not be ashamed. They spread eleven cubits past the *Beis Hakapores*: They spread because of the lack of space and would be scattered along the entire eleven cubits of the place where Yisrael were allowed to stand to the north and south, and went beyond those eleven cubits through the *Beis Hachalifos* between the *Heichal* and the walls of the *Azarah* north and south, and from there they stretched to the west, to the eleven cubits that were in between the *Beis Hakpores* and the western wall of the Azarah… Even though [the crowd was so large] that they spread eleven cubits behind *Beis Hakapores,* when everyone bowed down and came to the east of the *Mizbeach* from the Azarah, they all fit into the east side of the *Mizbeach* from within the *Azarah,* and were able to bow in front of the *Heichal* with plenty of room."

Page 38
Circling the *Mizbeach*
Each day they would circle the *Mizbeach* one time, and that day [Hoshana Rabba] seven times. We learn: Rabi Elazar says [they surrounded the *Mizbeach* while holding a] *lulav*, Rav Shmuel bar Nosson says in the name of Rabi Chanina, with the *aravah*. Rav Nachman also said in the name of Raba bar Avuha with the *aravah*. Rava said to Rav Yitzchak, the son of Raba bar Bar Chana, *bar uriya,* come and I will tell you a good thing that your father would say. The words of the Mishnah that say "each day they would circle the *Mizbeach* one time, and that day [Hoshana Rabba] seven times," your father said in the name of Rabi Elazar with the *lulav*. (*Sukkah* 43b). And the custom today is like the opinion that it was a *lulav*. (*Hilchesa Gevirta Sukkah* 4).

Who circled the *Mizbeach* and why
See *Rashi Sukkah* 43b. And the *Ra"n ibid.*
The pesukim recited while circling the *Mizbeach*---
'Each day they circled the *Mizbeach* once and said, '*Ana Hashem hoshia na, ana Hashem hatzlicha na.* Rabi Yehudah says, *ani vehu hoshia na.*' (*Mishnayos Sukkah* 4:5).

Times of *Tefillah* in the *Beis Hamikdash* on Sukkos
Rabi Yehoshua ben Chananya said: When we rejoiced at the *simchas beis hasho'evah* we did not see sleep with our eyes. How? The first hour – the *Tamid* of morning, from there, to daven, from there - to the *Korban Mussaf*, from there – to *Tefillas Mussaf*, from there – to the *Beis Midrash*, – from there – to eat and drink, from there – to *Tefillas Minchah*, from there – to the *Tamid* of the evening, and from then on to the *simchas beis hasho'evah*." (*Sukkah* 53a).

Page 39
Entrance of Yisraelim to the *Ezras Kohanim* and around the *Heichal*
"Rav Yehudah said, Rav said: When Yisrael were *oleh regel* they were crowded when they stood together, but when they bowed there was plenty of space and the crowd spread as far as eleven cubits behind the *Beis Hakapores*. What does this mean? Even though [the crowd was so large] that they spread eleven cubits behind *Beis Hakapores,* because it was so tightly packed, when they bowed, they had space, and that is one of the ten miracles that occurred in the *Mikdash*." (*Yoma* 21a)

Page 40
***Shir Shel Yom* of Sukkos**
"On Rosh Hashahah he says: '*Kol ha'amim tiku chaf.*' On Yom Kippur: '*Barchi nafshi* and *Mimaamakim karasicha Hashem.*' On Sukkos: '*Noda biyehudah.*' On the eighth day: '*Lamnatzeach al hashminis.*' (*Maseches Sofrim* 19:2)

Page 43
The *brachah* on eating a *shelamim*
See *Rashi Pesachim* 121a.

Page 44
The light at the *simchas beis hasho'evah* and the wicks
"From the worn pants of the Kohanim and from the belts, they would make wicks and would light them. There wasn't a courtyard in Yerushalayim that was not illuminated by the light of the *Shoevah*." (*Mishnayos Sukkah* 5:3)

Page 45

Who were the dancers

"Chassidim and *anshei maaseh* would dance before them with torches of light in their hands, and would say words of praise and song." (*Mishnayos Sukkah* 5:4)

Drawing *Ruach Hakodesh* from there

"Rabi Yehoshua ben Levi said: Why was it called *Beis Shoevah*? Because from there they drew *ruach hakodesh*, as it says '*Usheavtem mayim besasson mimaayanei hayeshuah*.' Rabi Yonah said: Yona ben Amitai was one of the *olei regel*, and he entered the *simchas beis hasho'evah* and the *ruach hakodesh* rested on him." (Yerushalmi Sukkah 5:1)

Page 46

Leviim orchestra

"Chassidim and *anshei maaseh* would dance before them with torches of light in their hands, and would say words of praise and song." And the Leviim with violins and harps and cymbals and trumpets and countless of other instruments, on the fifteen stairs descending from the *Ezras Yisrael* to the *Ezras Nashim* (corresponding to the fifteen *Shir Hamaalos* in *Tehillim*) upon which the Leviim stood with their instruments and said praise." (*Mishnayos Sukkah* 5:4)

The songs at the *simchas beis hasho'evah*

Chazal teach us: There were those who said: 'Fortunate are our younger years that did not embarrass our older years.' These are the *chassidim* and *anshei maaseh*. And there were those that said: "Fortunate is our old age that atoned for our childhood." Those were the *baalei teshuvah*. These and these both said, "Fortunate is he who has never sinned, and he who has sinned, should repent and he will be forgiven." We learn in a *braisa*: It is said of Hillel Hazaken, when he would rejoice at the *simchas beis hasho'evah,* he would say as follows: "If I am here, then everything is here, and if I am not here, then who is here?" He would also say: "The place where I want to go, that is where my legs take me.

If you come to My house, then I will come to your house. If you don't come to My house, then I will not come to your house, as it says, *Bechol hamakom asher azkir es Shemi avo elecha uveirachticha."* (*Sukkah* 53a)

Page 47

Dance with the torches

"Chazal say: It is said of Rabban Shimon ben Gamliel, when he rejoiced at the *simchas beis hasho'evah,* he would take eight torches of fire and throw one and catch one [juggle] and they would never touch each other." (*Sukkah 53a*)

Page 48

Time of the *simchah*

Rabi Yehoshua ben Chananya said: When we rejoiced at the *simchas beis hasho'evah* we did not see sleep with our eyes. How? The first hour – the *Tamid* of morning, from there, to daven, from there – to the *Korban Mussaf*, from there – to *Tefillas Mussaf*, from there – to the *Beis Midrash*, – from there – to eat and drink, from there – to *Tefillas Minchah*, from there – to the *Tamid* of the evening, and from then on to the *simchas beis hasho'evah*." (*Sukkah* 53a).

Page 49

Beating with the *aravah* on the seventh day only

"On the day when the *aravah* was used to beat the floor, the seventh day of Yom Tov, every one in the nation took from there one or more stalks, and hit the floor or a vessel with them, two or three times, without a *brachah,* because it is only a *minhag nevi'im*." (*Hilchesa Gevirta, Sukkah 4)* See also the *Rambam, Hilchos Lulav,* 7:22, but his language is not clear.

Page 50

The *nusach* when taking leave of the *Mizbeach*

"That day [Hoshana Rabba] they would circle the *Mizbeach* seven times. When they left, what did they say? "*Yofi lecha Mizbeach, yofi lecha Mizbeach*." Rabi Eliezer said, "*Le'Kah velach Mizbeach, Le'Kah velach Mizbeach*." (*Sukkah 45a*)

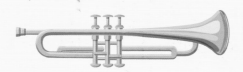